Conten

G000152889

The Wind

The wind has such a rainy sound
Moaning through the town,
The sea has such a windy sound –
Will the ships go down?

The apples in the orchard
Tumble from their tree –
Oh, will the ships go down, go down,
In the windy sea?

Christina Rossetti

Rain Magic

Gentle breeze is the father of rain,
Soft wind is the father of cloudburst,
Rain will not drench me today;
Rain will pack its belongings and go away.
    The antelope is humming,
    The buffalo is grumbling,
    The pig grunts in its belly.
Words have angered the red monkey,
But today he was given the right words
And his anger will disappear.

Yoruba

Aunty Betty

slip-slop
slip-slop

that's the sound my
Aunty Betty makes in her
big, baggy slippers

slip-slop
slip-slop

she never goes outside
the house, they say
it's agora-something

but I always call on
my way to school, she's a
brilliant cook and
she laughs a lot

I like my Aunty Betty
even if she's
not so good to look at

slip-slop
slip-slop.

Joan Poulson

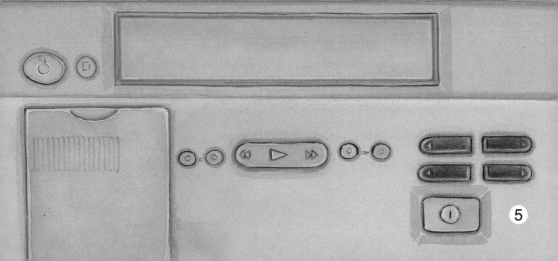

Home Alone

Mum's got a telly of her own
Dad's got a telly of his own
Baby got a telly of his own
Little sister got a telly of her own.

Cat got a telly of her own
Mouse got a telly of his own
I got a telly of my own
To make me feel at home.

Benjamin Zephaniah

The Tin Can Band

Oh, the tin can band,
Oh, the tin can band!
It's the dinniest band
In the big bright land.
It's a sing-song band, it's a bing-bong band.
It's a miss-a-beat, have-a-treat, skippy-feet
    band,
As we march along with our pots and pans,
And we bing and bong on our old tin cans.

We're a-singing and a-songing to the
    binging and the bonging.
We're escaping and a-skipping out
On every hand.

And it sounds like a battle
When our tin cans rattle,
When our tin cans rattle
And our tin cans clang.

Yes, it's sounding like the prattle and the
tattle of a battle
Like a merry monster cannon going
BANG, BANG, BANG!

Though silence falls when the band's
gone by,
And the street is bare to the hills and sky,
There's a nitter and a natter,
And a tiny tinny patter,
Like a whisper (only crisper)
Like a tin toy's sigh,
And a flutter like a mutter,
Like a sunny sort of stutter,
Going giggling down the gutter
Where the funny echoes die.

Margaret Mahy

Wicked Thoughts

The meanest girl I've ever met
Is Mary Ellen Wright,
And if a lion came along and
Ate her with one bite,
I'd cry and cry and cry and cry.
(But just to be polite).

Judith Viorst

Wars

When I was in Grade Two, I said to
    my father,
"I think wars are wrong!
People should be told to stop all this
    fighting right now.
If I were crowned Queen of the World,
I'd make wars against the law."
My father said I had something there,
But he didn't seem terribly excited.
I could not understand him.

Then I went upstairs and caught my
    sister Marilyn
Playing with my new paper dolls
    without my permission!

We had a war.

Jean Little

Junk

We made this thing of jumbly junk
Four legs, three arms, six eyes.
And when we'd hammered forty nails
It moved, to our surprise.

It walked about and creaked and clicked
And even shook its head,
But when it spoke with rusty voice
"Goodbye" was all it said.

Libby Hathorn

Talks with my Skateboard

It's really neat
When skateboards speak!
And what do you know?
Mine says *Go!*
You mightn't believe me
But this is quite true –
When someone says *Don't!*
My skateboard says *Do!*
When someone says *Hey,*
this kid is a fool
My skateboard replies
No, this kid is cool.
Shoes might squeak
And kettles might shriek
But it's really neat
When skateboards speak.

Libby Hathorn

11

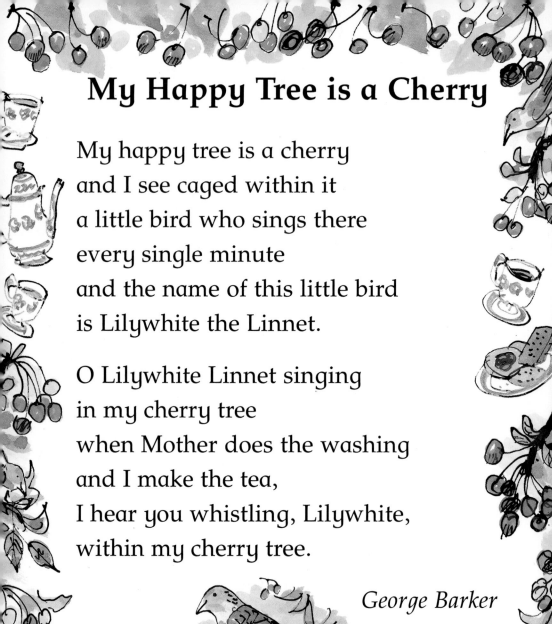

My Happy Tree is a Cherry

My happy tree is a cherry
and I see caged within it
a little bird who sings there
every single minute
and the name of this little bird
is Lilywhite the Linnet.

O Lilywhite Linnet singing
in my cherry tree
when Mother does the washing
and I make the tea,
I hear you whistling, Lilywhite,
within my cherry tree.

George Barker

Woodpecker

Woodpecker is rubber-necked
But has a nose of steel.
He bangs his head against the wall
And cannot even feel.

When Woodpecker's jack-hammer head
Starts up its dreadful din
Knocking the dead bough double dead
How do his eyes stay in?

Pity the poor dead oak that cries
In terrors and in pains.
But pity more Woodpecker's eyes
And bouncing rubber brains.

Ted Hughes

Every Game's a Home Game with my Footy Family

Grandad's in the goal
Dad's in defence
Mother's in midfield
Baby's on the bench

Sister's centre forward
Brother's at the back
Cousin is the coach
Auntie's in attack

Nana is the manager
and just because I missed
a penalty last home match
I'm on the transfer list.

Paul Cookson

Pig Sings

Pig's song of courtship

Grobble Snort
Blurp Blort
Screep Uggle
Slop Snuffle
Honk Squelch
Flubber Belch
Wee   Say
Wee   You
Wee   Love
Wee   Me

John Mole

Bedtime Song

The stars above are glittering
The moon is gleaming bright
And noisy cats are singing songs
Down in the yard tonight
MIAOW WOW WOW
WOW WOW

People in their dressing-gowns
In houses far and near
Are leaning from their window sills
They're horrified to hear
MIAOW WOW WOW
WOW WOW

But we don't want a lullaby
We prefer a din
Noisy cats are what we like –
All join in!
MIAOW WOW WOW
WOW WOW
WOW WOW

Quentin Blake

Lazy

How dare they
call me lazy
when all the things
that I have done
are scattered

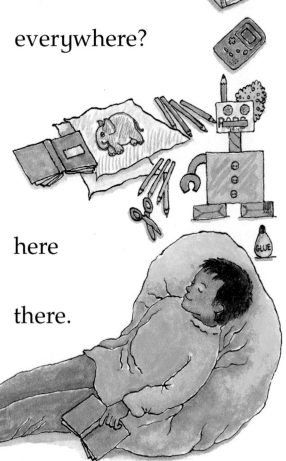

everywhere?

The fact that
they still
need doing
is
neither

here

nor

there.

Pauline Stewart

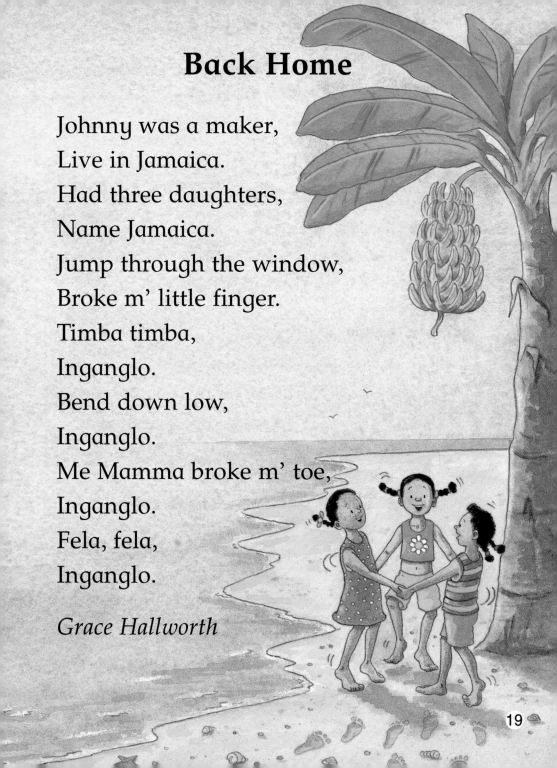

Back Home

Johnny was a maker,
Live in Jamaica.
Had three daughters,
Name Jamaica.
Jump through the window,
Broke m' little finger.
Timba timba,
Inganglo.
Bend down low,
Inganglo.
Me Mamma broke m' toe,
Inganglo.
Fela, fela,
Inganglo.

Grace Hallworth

The Blackbirds' Party

The blackbirds gave a party
And invited everybody.
The grasshopper came with a hop,
 hop, hop,
For a while the music had to stop.
The snail was too slow
So he almost didn't go,
With a slop, slow, slop, slow, slop.

The snake hissed and wriggled
And the parrots giggled
As his body wiggled with a plop!
The bumble-bees drummed,
The humming-birds hummed,
While a cat's guitar strummed.
The dogs barked and joked,
Drums beat and broke
And a giant cherry-cake spoke!

The mice did a dance
Fell in a trance
The cats didn't give them a glance.
The squirrels made a riddle,
A dog played a fiddle,
And the blackbirds flew away with
a song,
With a song,
The blackbirds flew away
with a song!

Faustin Charles

Family Tree

My sister's mother's
husband's brother's
nephew's sister's
brother's ... ME!

Lindsay MacCrae

Index of poem features